ROSE RIGDEN'S WILDSIDE

Published by Footloose Enterprises Limited
P.O. Box 914
Cambridge, 3450, New Zealand.
Email: info@thewildside.co.nz
Web: www.thewildside.co.nz

ISBN 978-0-473-11862-4

Someone once said 'game viewing' consists of two groups of people. Some shouting 'there there" and the other shouting "where where?". For many of us looking at animals and birds is a passion whether in bushland, desert or by the sea. We watch by day or listen by night and love to observe the behaviour and habits of all creatures great and small.

Our Artist, Rose Rigden has spent many years doing just that, and this book is her perception that maybe, we as humans are not so far removed from the animals, as we think!

Discover not just the 'wildside' but the wildly funny side, when the watcher becomes the watched, and the true nature of the beast is revealed!

Rose lives with her husband in a small village near the Chimanimani Mountains on Zimbabwe's eastern border. Born in Mutare, Rose received her formal training at the Durban Art College, South Africa.

She has gained world wide recognition and awards through major public exhibitions. Her great love of painting is reflected in the expertise that she demonstrates in her detailed landscapes and portraits.

THE ARTIST

Rose Rigden

Moving away from the formality of fine art, she reveals the quixotic side of her nature. Rose enjoys turning 'sense' into 'nonsense' and injects laughter into the most serious of situations! Over the years, her exposure to the wild animals and their habitats inevitably led her to depicting these scenes, with the animals exhibiting non-conformist behaviour and adopting some of our attitudes and phobias.
Man and the Animals!
The next time you peer from your hiding place at the creatures that share our land and sea, maybe your binoculars, camera lens or glasses will become a little 'Rose' tinted as well!!

Some of us spend hours looking very hard for the elusive game.

"Haven't seen a thing all day"

We sit down, patiently waiting at waterholes.

"Oh will you be quiet...I'm trying to focus."

Rose Rigden 99

Drive in all terrain vehicles with accomplished guides ... and

peer into long grass, looking for the unexpected!

Sometimes we trek, backpacking with the best of companions…

Camping in the wild, getting close to Mother Nature…

is a thrill, even to nervous types.

"Sleep tight."

From shady spots, keenly observing all activity…

to climbing into tree platforms…

we share in the harmony of nature.

Sometimse insects can be a problem!

Habitually, we choose the same time each year to watch the animals.

"I'll get back to you, I'm in the middle of this migration thing!"

Enjoying the afternoon trip into the bush, when there is so much activity!

"Wake up you guys, its sundowner time!"

Rose Rigden

"A herd of *what* coming?"

"He won't budge… says he's sick of being hounded by paparazzi!"

We must understand their habits.

"I think it's 'someone' he ate!"

"Yummy, just a light oil dressing!"

"It never fails, the old log trick!"

Some of us look for the 'Big Five'.

We celebrate when we find them.

"And they call *us* wildlife!"

Getting acclimatised to the bush and all its little surprises…

usually takes some time for adjustment.

"Steady on dear, it's on the endangered list!"

Playing with the animals in their environment can be fun…

"Alone at last!"

"Close your eyes Percival"

"The next tourist to call me a leopard gets to be lunch!"

"It says here, that you have a rudimentary tail and a convoluted brain!"

We exchange behavioural patterns.

"It's what we suspected, he's become a vegetarian!"

"Don't mention that leopards aren't supposed to change their spots."

BEACHED

weaknesses.

"You can never say no to another Marula can you?"

"I see the tourists are back!"

tastes.

"Don't you just loved them peeled?"

"It's no use, even drinking doesn't help me forget!"

Competing with each other…

"We can't miss with that crowd!"

"Its nature's way of keeping numbers down!"

king time!

Man tries to make provision…

"Its for you dear … Animal Rights again!"

by introducing new ideas.

"Psst!… want to buy some take-a-ways?"

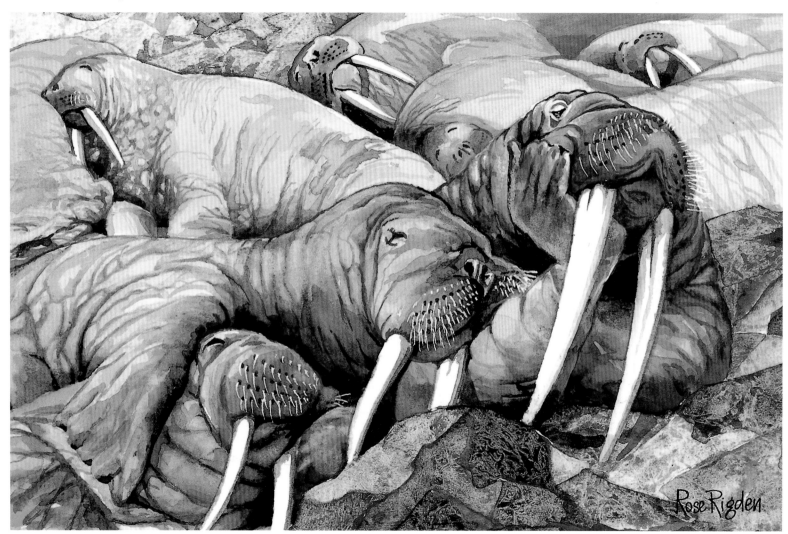

"Wish you were here!"

others are not.

Suddenly, the forest seemed a safer place!

"Where's my cricket bat Mum?"

common to all of us.

"Yeah, I've been grounded again!"

Keeping up appearances…

"O.K. girls, turn on the charm"

"It's not working is it?"

"Hmph! … crested is she?"

Fiercely competitive…

and progressive.

"There must be an easier way!"

enjoying the fruits of our labour.

"Next he'll be wanting a carving knife!"

And we party anywhere!

"It was the only place that wasn't booked"

"I snuk up behind that one whilst he was re-loading"

are over the top!

"Goody bar snacks."

Whale watching

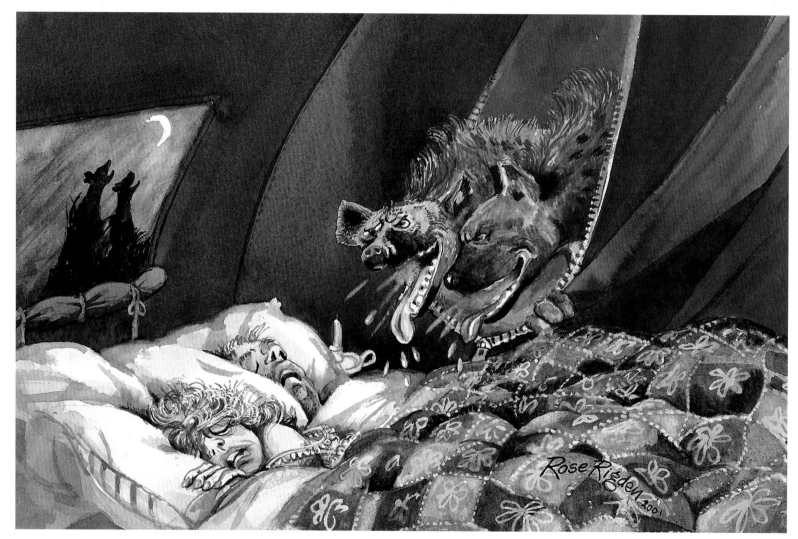

"Did you remember to brush your teeth dear?"

"Only a mother could love <u>that</u> chick!"

"I said, 'Are you having a nice time?'"

"Hardly regal are they?"

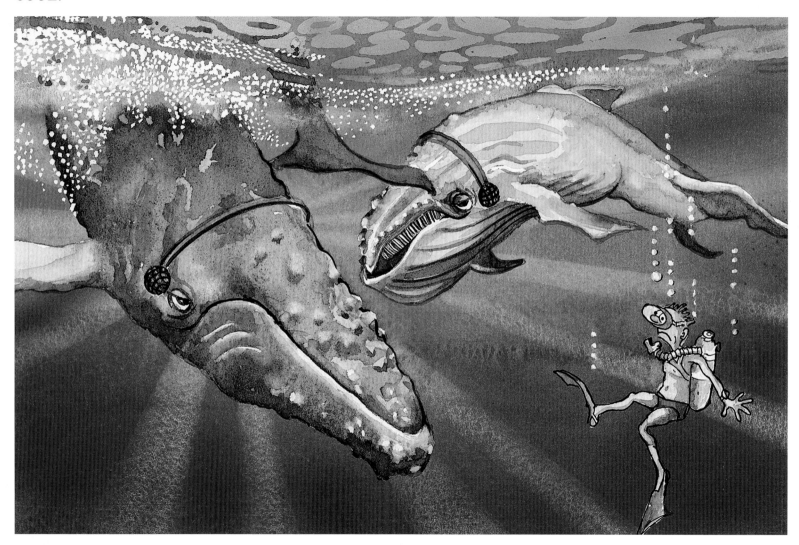

"Don't you just love it when some fool yells "Migration Time"!

leave time for reflection.

"And they call <u>us</u> 'wildlife'!"

"Yeah! That bite really spoils the skin!"

we often think of our loved ones.

"By the way dear, how is your Mother?"

"And they call *us*, gannets!"

at favourite watering holes.

"Are you sure you weren't dreaming Darling?"

When you bask in the scenic beauty of the bush…

"Looks like a good place for a picnic!"

Don't take chances!

"I'm sure I gave the tickets to you."

By small upsets.

"Nothing biting today......"

"He never gives up, does he!"